MW00634954

2 Practice Tests
for the
NNAT®
GRADE 1
(NNAT3 Level B)

Origins Publications helps students develop their higher-order thinking skills while also improving their chances of admission into gifted and accelerated learner programs.

Our goal is to unleash and nurture the genius in every student. We do this by offering educational and test prep materials that are fun, challenging and provide a sense of accomplishment.

Please contact us with any questions.
info@originspublications.com

Copyright© 2019 by Origins Publications
Written and Edited by: Gifted and Talented NNAT Test Prep Team

ISBN: 978-1-948255-78-3

Origins Publications, New York, NY, USA

BONUS

DOWNLOAD YOUR NNAT PRACTICE TEST/S

IN

COLOR

If you also want the COLOR version of this book, please go to the following link to download it!

Please visit
https://originstutoring.lpages.co/nnat110

to access the color version of the practice tests.

Contents

Part 1: Introduction to the NNAT®

This book offers an overview of the types of questions on the Naglieri Nonverbal Ability Test (NNAT) Level B, test-taking strategies to improve performance, and two full-length practice NNAT® Level B practice tests that students can use to assess their knowledge and practice their test-taking skills.

Who Takes the NNAT® Level B?

The NNAT® Level B is often used as an assessment tool or admissions test in 1st grade for entry into 2nd grade of gifted and talented programs and highly-competitive schools. The NNAT® Level B is also used as an assessment tool by teachers to figure out which students would benefit from an accelerated or remedial curriculum.

When Does the NNAT® Take Place?

This depends on the school district you reside in or want to attend. Check with the relevant school/ district to learn more about test dates and the application/ registration process.

NNAT® Level B Overview

The NNAT® is designed to assess the cognitive skills that relate to academic success in school for students between four and 18. The questions on the NNAT®2 consist of geometric figures, shapes, and symbols. A child must use visual reasoning and logical thinking to decipher the answers. The test does not require a child to be able to read, write or speak in the English Language.

Length

The NNAT®2 has 48 multiple-choice questions and offers both an online version and a paper and pencil test. It takes approximately 30 minutes to complete.

Format

The official NNAT test has only 3 colors: blue, orange and green. (The color green was recently added in the most recent edition of the NNAT).

Part 2: How to Use this Book

The NNAT® is an important test and the more a student is familiar with the questions on the exam, the better she will fare when taking the test.

This book will help your student get used to the format and content of the test so s/he will be adequately prepared and feel confident on test day.

Inside this book, you will find:

- Overview of each question type on the test and teaching tips to help your child approach each question type strategically and with confidence.

- 2 full-length NNAT® Level B practice tests and answer keys.

Part 3. Test Prep Tips and Strategies

Firstly, and most importantly, commit to make the test preparation process a stress-free one. A student's ability to keep calm and focused in the face of challenge is a quality that will benefit him or her throughout his or her academic life.

Be prepared for difficult questions from the get-go! There will be a certain percentage of questions that are very challenging for all children. It is key to encourage students to use all strategies available when faced with challenging questions. And remember that a student can get quite a few questions wrong and still do very well on the test.

Before starting the practice test, go through the sample questions and read the general test prep strategies provided at the beginning of the book. They will help you guide your student as he or she progresses through the practice test.

The following strategies may also be useful as you help your child prepare:

Before You Start

- Find a quiet, comfortable spot to work free of distractions.
- Tell your student you will be doing some fun activities, and that this is an opportunity for you to spend some enjoyable time together.
- Show your student how to perform the simple technique of shading (and erasing) bubbles.

During Prep

- Encourage your student to carefully consider all the answer options before selecting one. Tell him or her there is only ONE answer.
- If your student is stumped by a question, she or he can use the process of elimination. First, encourage your student to eliminate obviously wrong answers to narrow down the answer choices. If your student is still in doubt after using this technique, tell him or her to guess as there are no points deducted for wrong answers.
- Encourage your student to visualise the correct answer in the empty box before checking the answer options.

- If challenged by a question, ask your student to explain why he or she chose a specific answer. If the answer was incorrect, this will help you identify where your student is stumbling. If the answer was correct, asking your child to articulate her reasoning aloud will help reinforce the concept.
- Review all the questions your student answered incorrectly, and explain to your student why the answer is incorrect. Have your student attempt these questions again a few days later to see if he or she now understands the concept.
- Encourage your student to do his or her best, but take plenty of study breaks. Start with 10-15 minute sessions. Your student will perform best if she views these activities as fun and engaging, not as exercises to be avoided.

When to Start Preparing?

Every family and student will approach preparation for this test differently. There is no 'right' way to prepare; there is only the best way for a particular child and family. We suggest students take one full-length practice test and spend 6-8 hours reviewing NNAT® practice questions.

If you have limited time to prepare, spend most energy reviewing areas where your student is encountering the majority of problems.

As they say, knowledge is power! Preparing for the NNAT® will certainly help your student avoid anxiety and make sure she does not give up too soon when faced with unfamiliar and perplexing questions.

Part 4: Question Types and Teaching Tips

The NNAT® Level B is comprised of four different question types:

Pattern Completion
Reasoning by Analogy
Serial Reasoning
Spatial Visualization

Each question type involves the following steps:

- The student is presented with a picture of a matrix.
- The student must observe and detect the relationship among the parts of the matrix.
- The student must solve the problem based on the information shown to her within the matrix, and choose the correct answer from five possible options.

Pattern Completion

With this question type, the student is presented with a design in a rectangle. Inside the large rectangle contianing the puzzle is a smaller white rectangle (with a question mark inside) representing a missing piece that completes the design. The student must choose the answer that best fits the inner rectangle so that the missing parts complete the design.

These questions are the most common question types found on the Level A and B tests, and are the easiest kinds of matrices in the exam.

Before each question in this section, say to your child:

"Look at the picture. A piece is missing where you see the question mark. Show me the piece that is missing in the answer choices."

After a few questions, your child will probably not need this prompt and will spontaneously point to or mark an answer.

SAMPLE QUESTION:

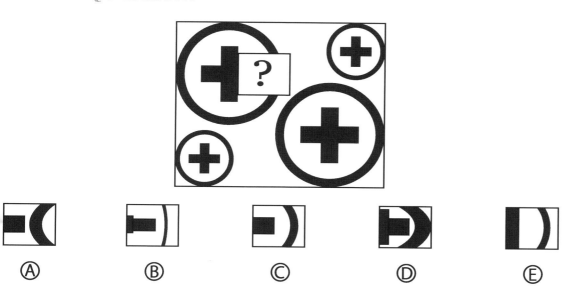

Ⓐ   Ⓑ   Ⓒ   Ⓓ   Ⓔ

Answer: C

TIPS:

Ask your student to complete the picture by continuing the correct lines and colors of the design into the empty box. Then, match the drawing with the correct answer choice.

Ask your student to note the color and design next to the corners of the empty box as this is a useful base to help identify the correct answer.

Go through each answer option and ask the student to visualize how each choice would fit the design.

Reasoning by Analogy

With this question type, the child is presented with a matrix of 4-6 boxes containing objects, usually geometric shapes.

To solve the problem, the child must determine how the object changes as it moves across the row and down the column in the matrix. The question may require that the student pay close attention to several aspects of the design (e.g: shading, color, shape) at the same time.

Before each question in this section, say to your student:

"Look at the picture. A piece is missing where you see the question mark. Show me the piece that is missing in the answer choices."

SAMPLE QUESTION:

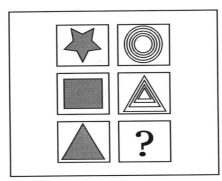

Ⓐ   Ⓑ   Ⓒ   Ⓓ   Ⓔ

Answer: B

TIPS:
Make sure your student knows key concepts that come up in these types of questions, including geometric concepts such as rotational symmetry, line symmetry, parts of a whole.

If your student is finding these items difficult, encourage her to discover the pattern by looking in each direction (horizontally and vertically).
• Ask: "How do the objects change in the first row? Do you see a pattern?Do the objects change in the same way in the second row? The third row?"
• Ask: "How do the objects change in the first column? Do you see a pat-tern? Do the objects change

in the same way in the second column? The third column?"

Encourage your student to isolate one element (e.g: outer shape, inner shape/s) and identify how it changes:
- Is the color/shading of the element changing as it moves?
- Is the element changing positions as it moves? Does it move up or down? Clockwise or counter-clockwise? Does it end up in the opposite (mirror) position?
- Does the element disappear and appear again as it move along the row/ column? Does it get bigger or smaller?

Encourage your student to make a prediction for the missing object and compare the description with the answer choices.

Serial Reasoning

With this question type, the student is shown a series of shapes that change across the rows and columns throughout the design. These questions require the student to understand how the objects in rows and columns relate to each other. The student must isolate and apply the rule/s in order to identify which object from the answer choices fits the empty box in the bottom right-hand corner of the matrix.

Before each question in this section, say to your student:

"Look at the picture. A piece is missing where you see the question mark. Show me the piece that is missing in the answer choices."

SAMPLE QUESTION:

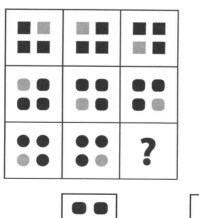

  Ⓐ   Ⓑ   Ⓒ   Ⓓ   Ⓔ

Answer: B

TIPS:
Encourage your student to discover the pattern by looking in each direction.
- Horizontally across the rows. Ask: "How do the objects change in the first row? Do you see a pattern? Do the objects change in the same way in the second row? The third row?"
- Vertically down the columns. Ask: "How do the objects change in the first column? Do you see a pattern? Do the objects change in the same way in the second column? The third column?"
- Diagonally (if the item is a 6-box matrix). Ask: "How do the objects change across the diagonal? Do you see a pattern?"

Encourage your student to isolate one element (e.g: outer shape, inner shape/s) and identify how it changes.
- How does the color/shading of the element change as it moves along the row/column?
- Does the element change positions as it moves along the row/column? Does it move up, down or around (i.e.: clockwise, counter-clockwise). Does the element move to the opposite position?
- Does the element get bigger, smaller or stay the same as it moves?
- Does the element disappear and appear again as you move along the row/column?

Spatial Visualization

With this question type, a student is presented with a series of objects that com-bine, invert, transform and/or rotate across rows and columns. The student must identify the rule for the top row of objects and then predict what will happen to objects in the second (or third) row. S/he must then select which object among the answer choices follows this rule and should go in the empty box in the matrix.

Spatial Visualization items are widely seen to be the most difficult, particularly when involving objects that intersect in ways that are hard to recognize or involve an object rotating.

Before each question in this section, say to your student:

"Look at the picture. A piece is missing where you see the question mark. Show me the piece that is missing in the answer choices."

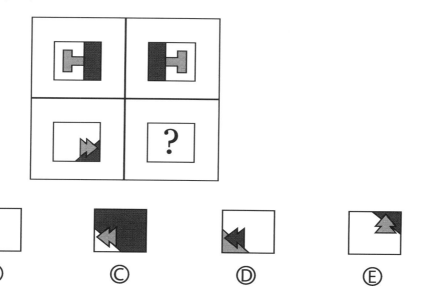

Answer: A

TIPS:
Ask your student to do some paper-folding projects. This will help her understand how objects on a folded piece of paper appear (and relate to each other) when the paper is opened.

Encourage your student to visualize -- observe, imagine and keep track of -- the changes in the geometric shapes as they move and then draw what she predicts she might see in the empty box.

Encourage your student to isolate one element (e.g: outer shape, inner shape/s) and identify how it changes.
- How does the color/shading of the element change as it moves along the row/column?
- Does the element change positions as it moves along the row/column?Does the element move to the opposite position?
- Does the element flip positions (e.g.: outer square becomes inner square or vice-versa)? Does the element go upside down?
- Does the element combine with another element?

NNAT® B
Practice Test One

NOTE: The NNAT® B level test is most often given to a child in a one- on-one setting, with the administrator reading the question to the child. In this practice test, you can take on the role of the administrator by reading the question to your student.

Answer bubble sheets can be found at the back of the book. Please make sure your student fills in each of the bubbles fully.

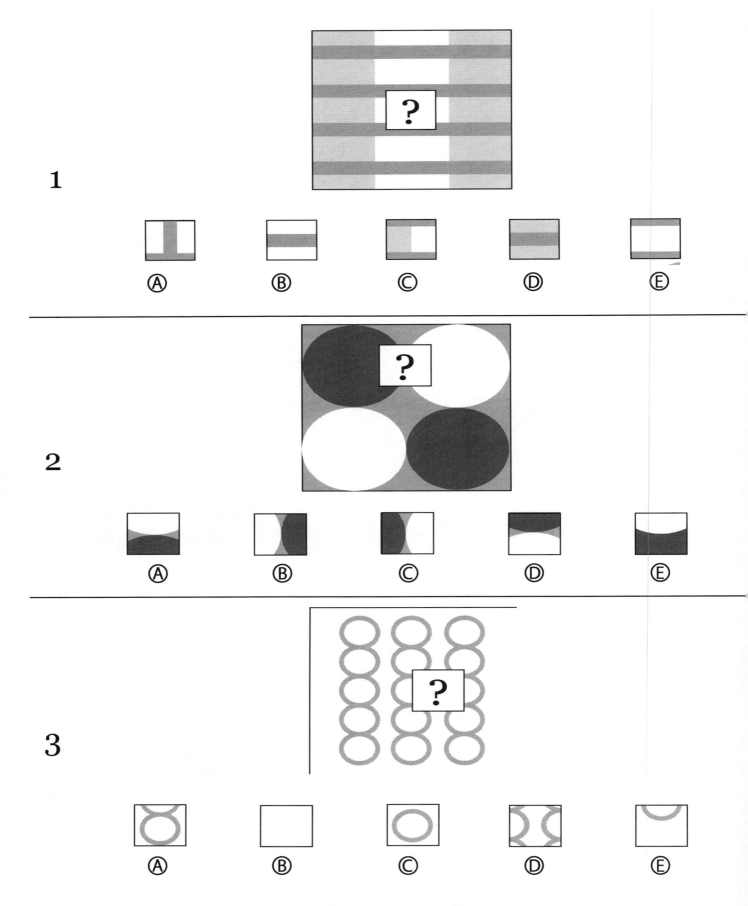

1

2

3

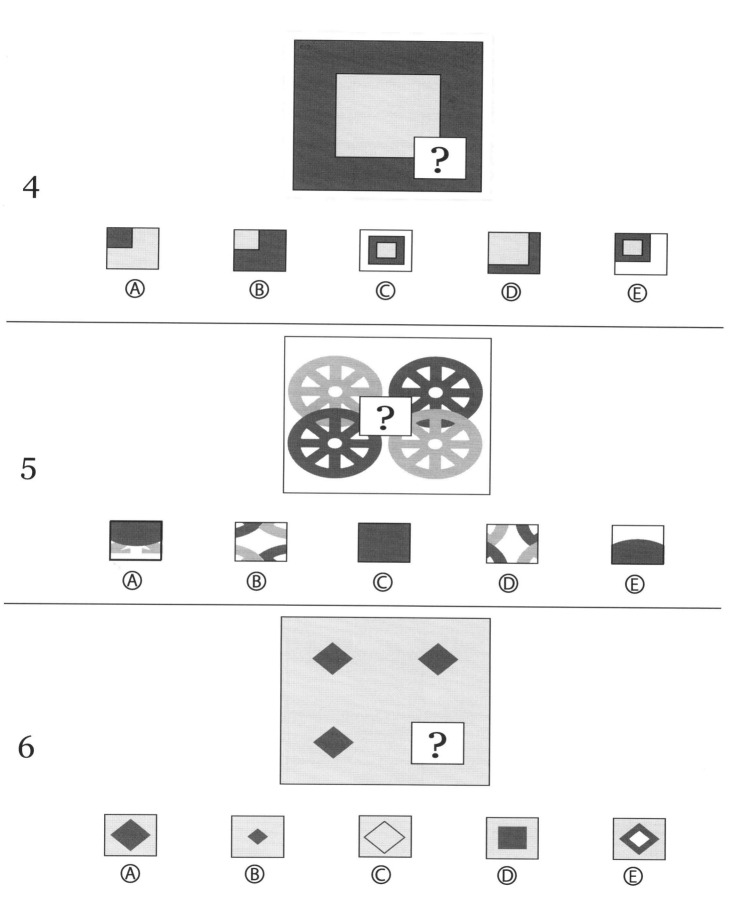

4

5

6

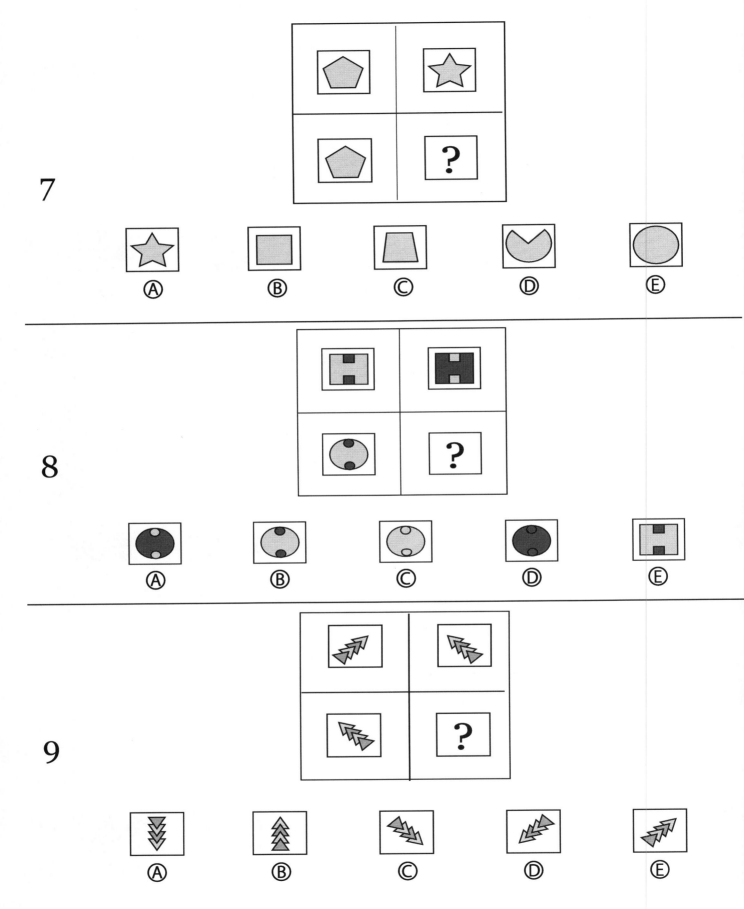

7

8

9

NNAT® Level B Test Prep Workbook

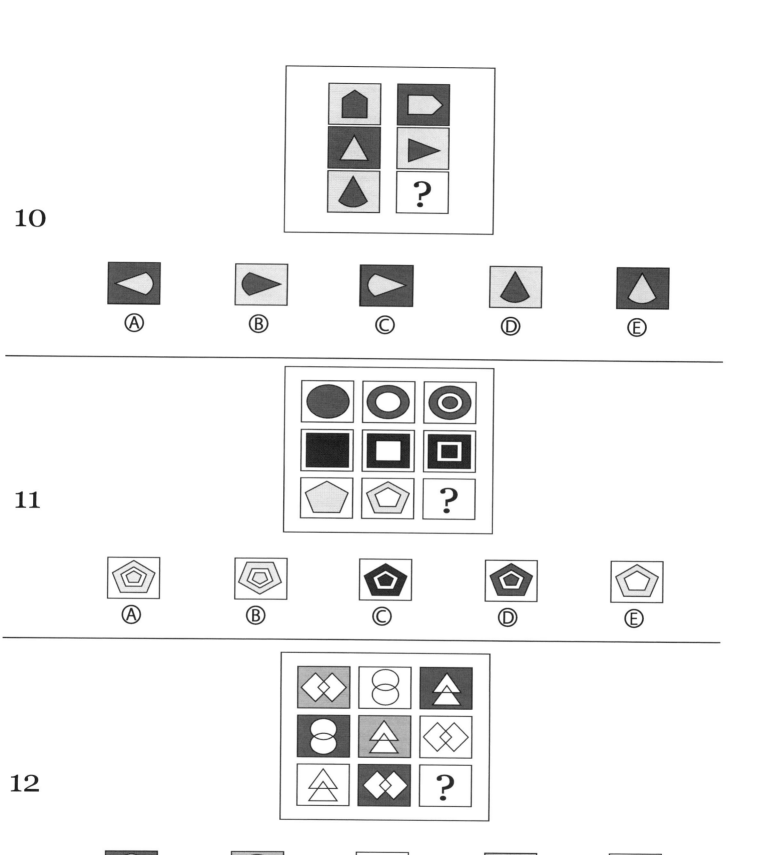

10

11

12

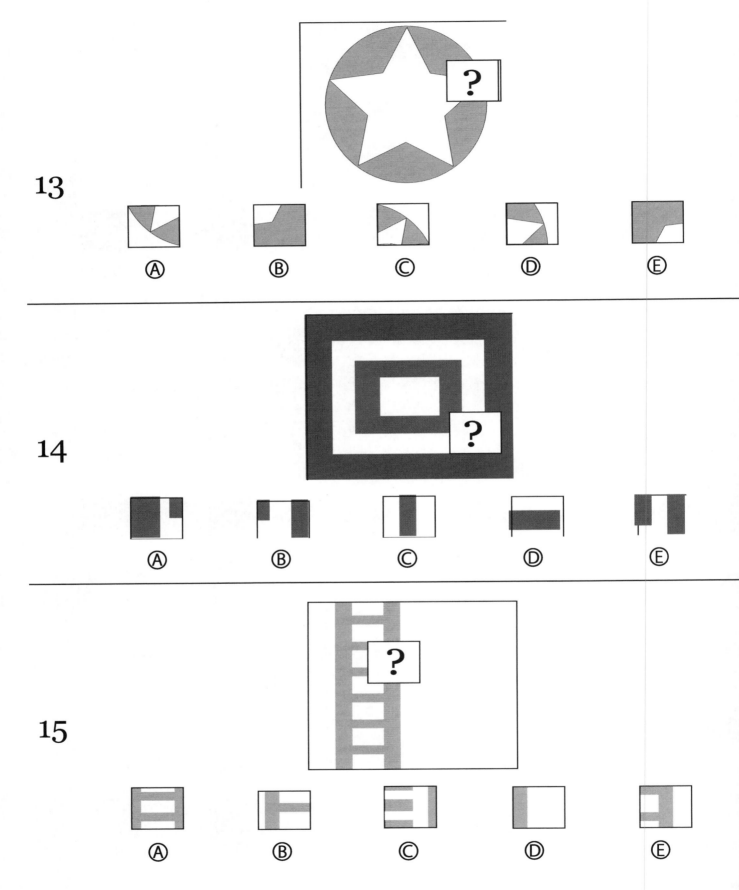

13

14

15

NNAT® Level B Test Prep Workbook

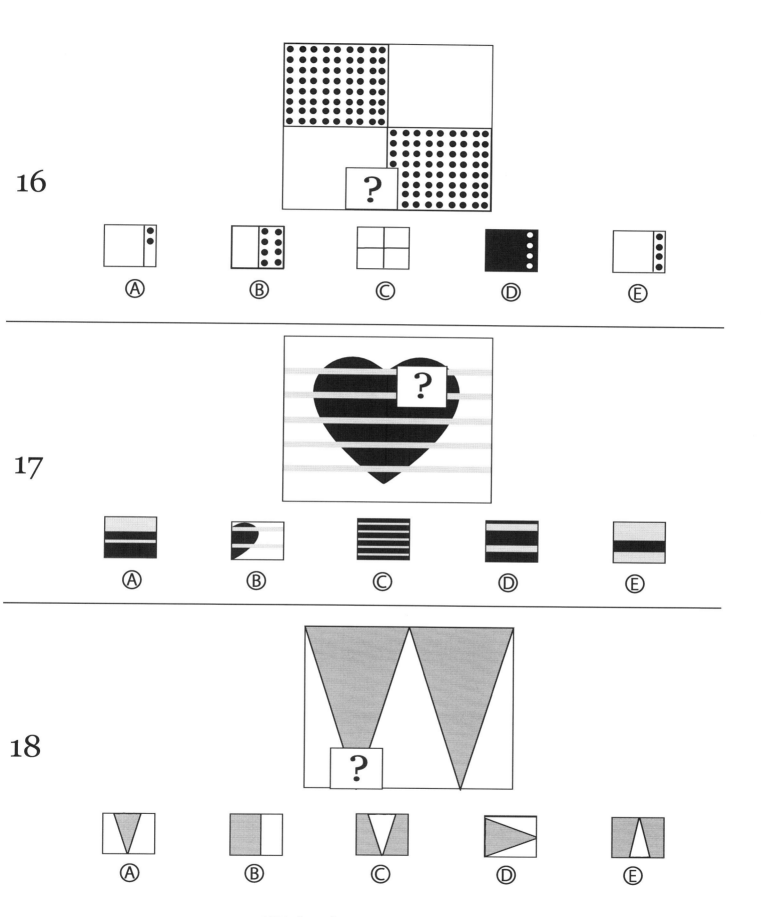

16

17

18

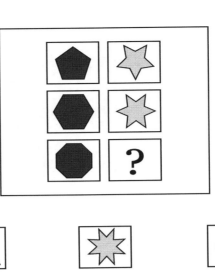

19

Ⓐ

Ⓑ

Ⓒ

Ⓓ

Ⓔ

20

Ⓐ

Ⓑ

Ⓒ

Ⓓ

Ⓔ

21

Ⓐ

Ⓑ

Ⓒ

Ⓓ

Ⓔ

NNAT® Level B Test Prep Workbook

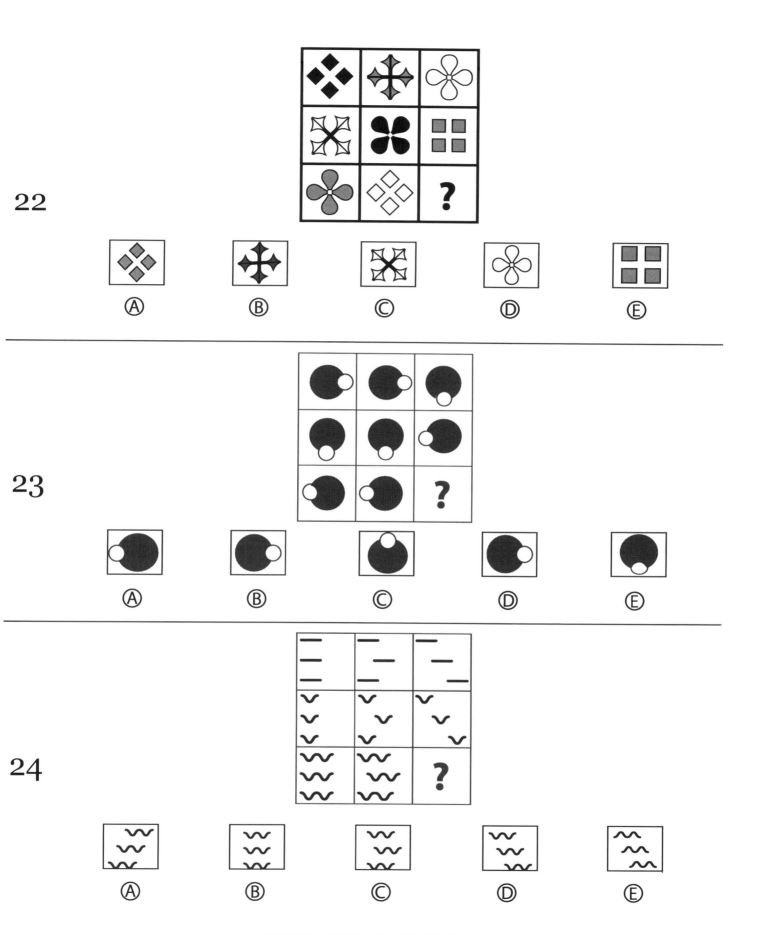

22

23

24

25

Ⓐ

Ⓑ

Ⓒ

Ⓓ

Ⓔ

26

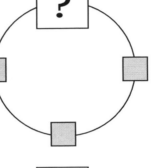

Ⓐ

Ⓑ

Ⓒ

Ⓓ

Ⓔ

27

Ⓐ

Ⓑ

Ⓒ

Ⓓ

Ⓔ

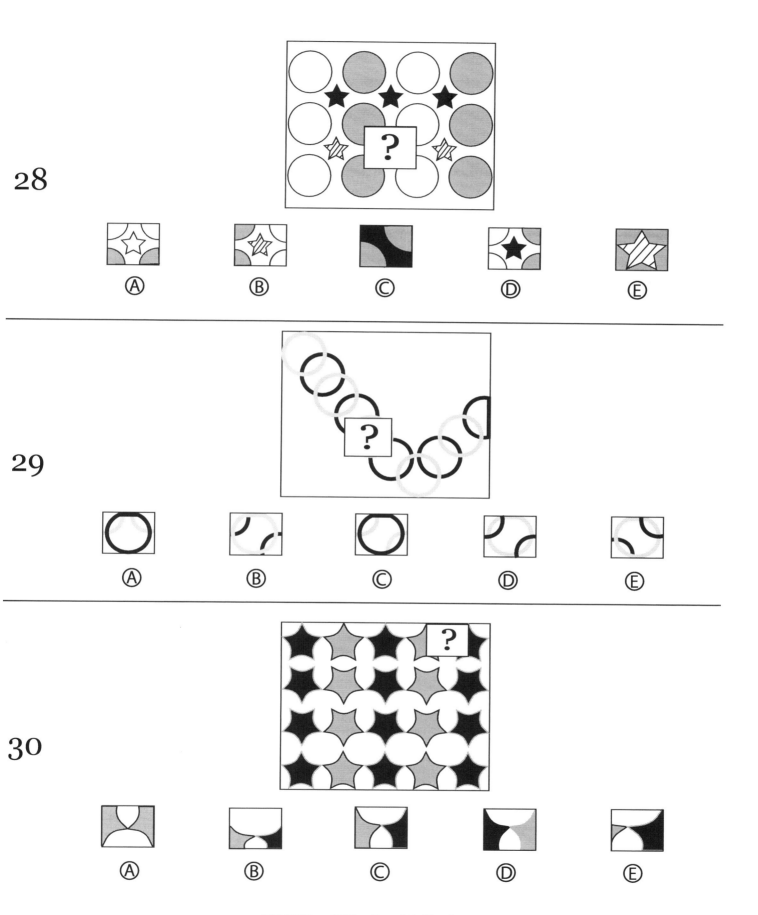

28

29

30

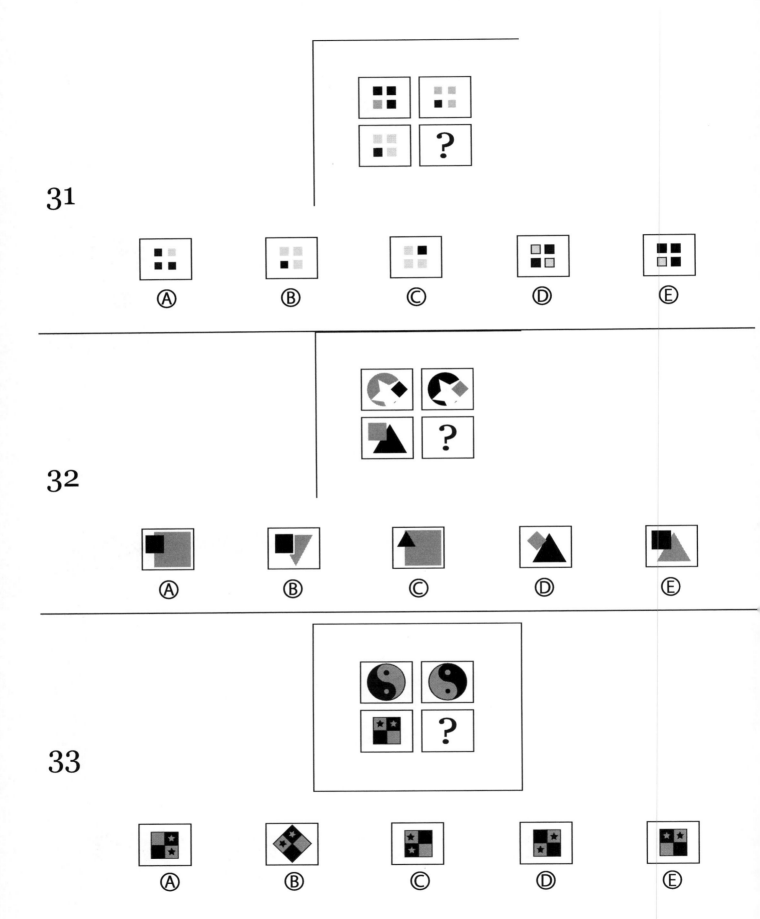

31

32

33

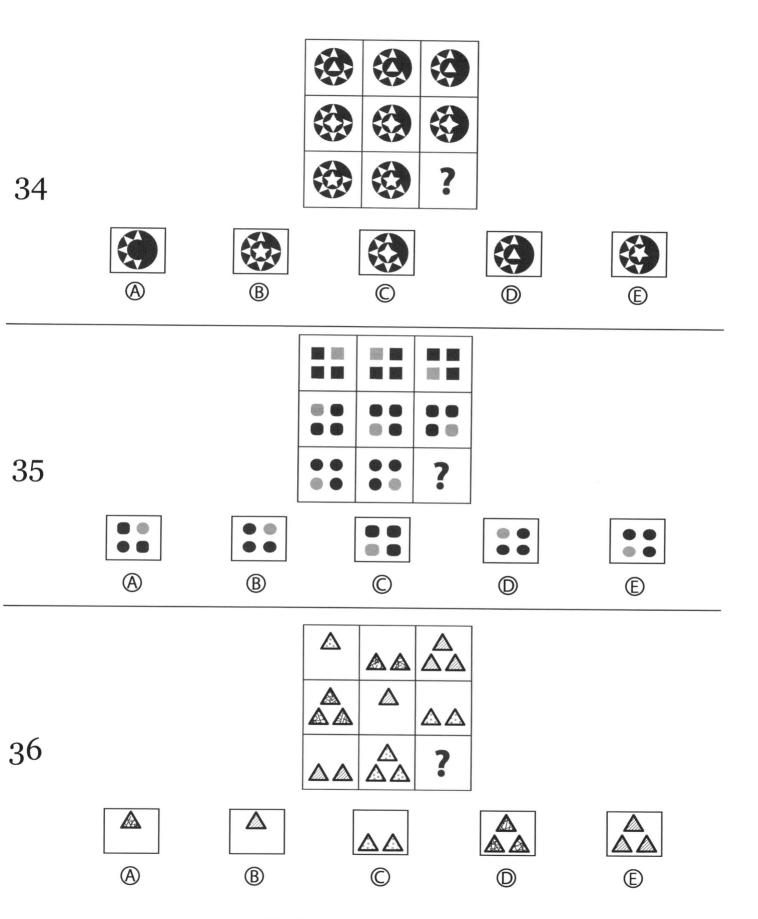

34

35

36

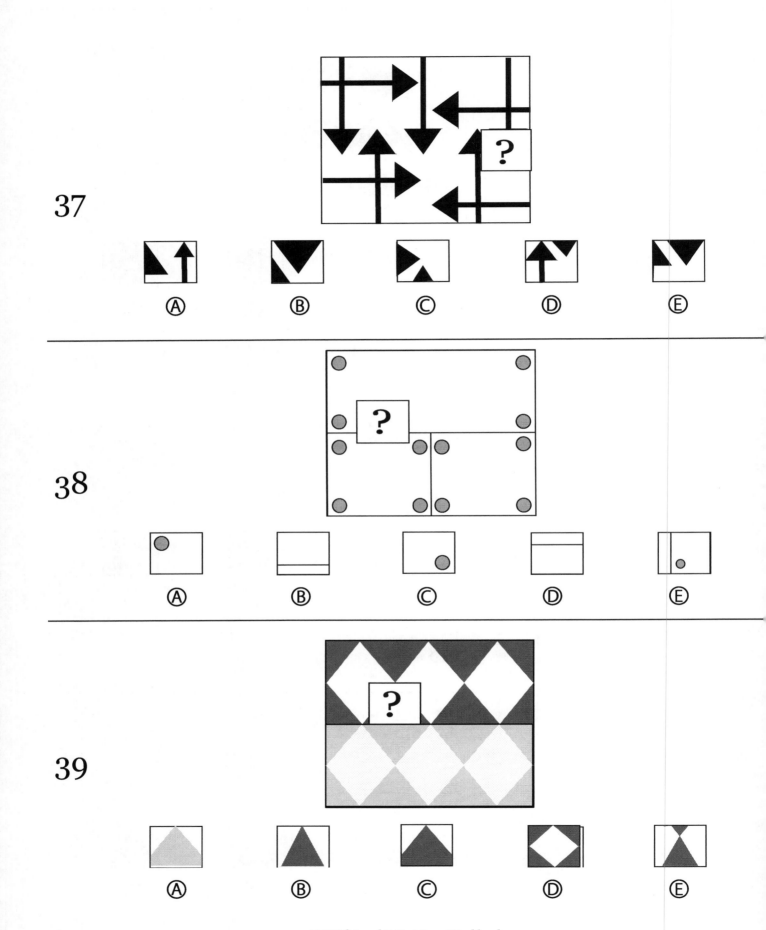

37

38

39

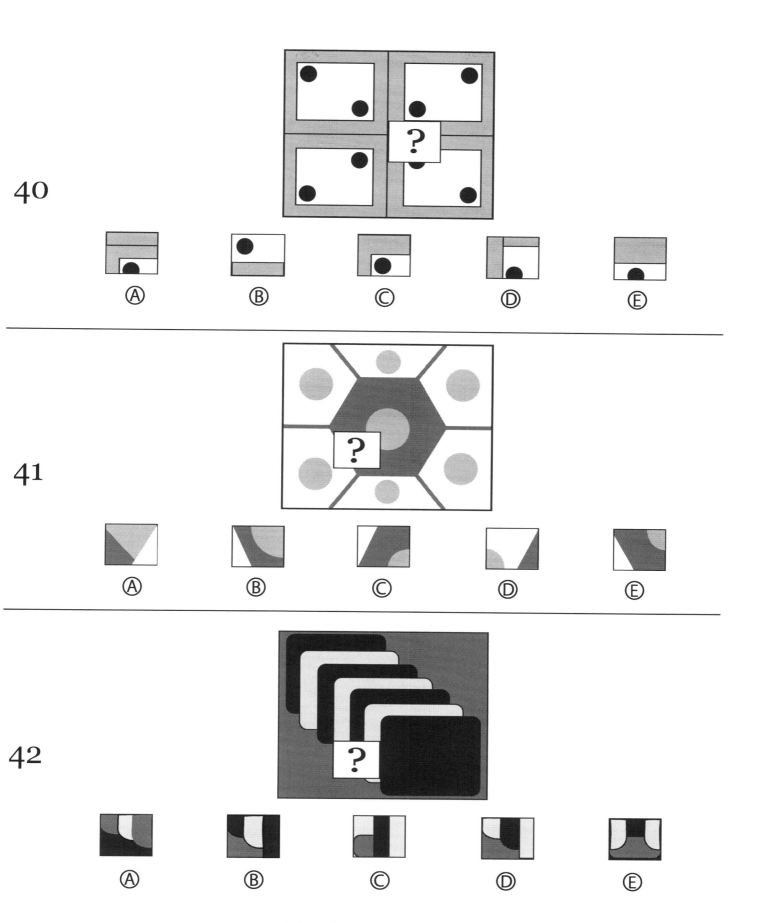

40

41

42

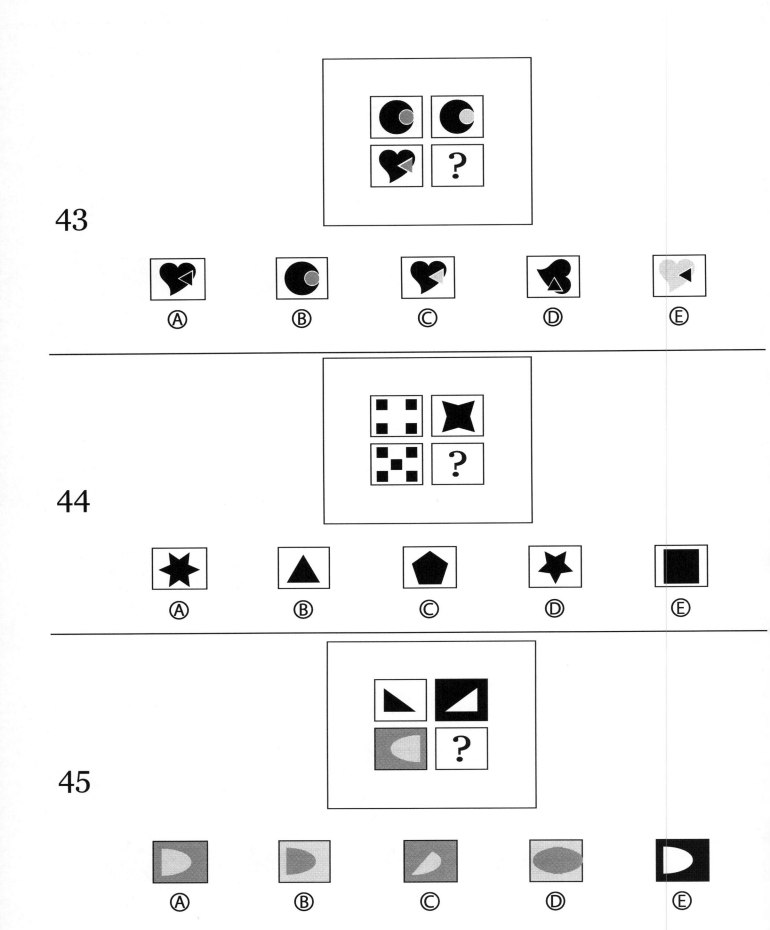

43

44

45

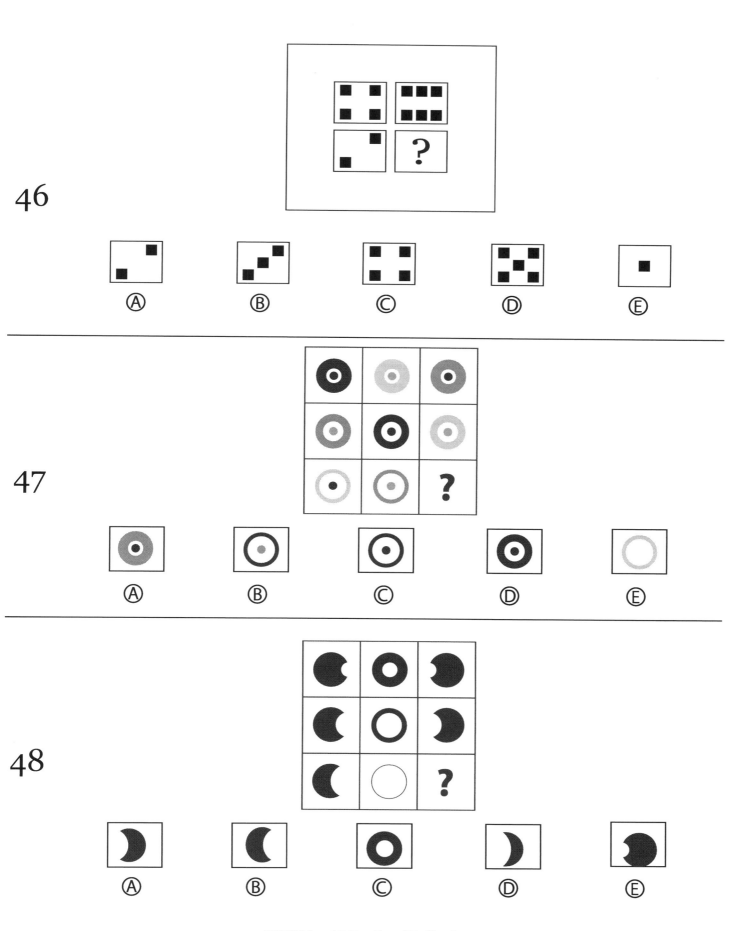

46

47

48

NNAT® B
Practice Test Two

NOTE: The NNAT® B level test is most often given to a child in a one- on-one setting, with the administrator reading the question to the child. In this practice test, you can take on the role of the administrator by reading the question to your student.

Answer bubble sheets can be found at the back of the book. Please make sure your student fills in each of the bubbles fully.

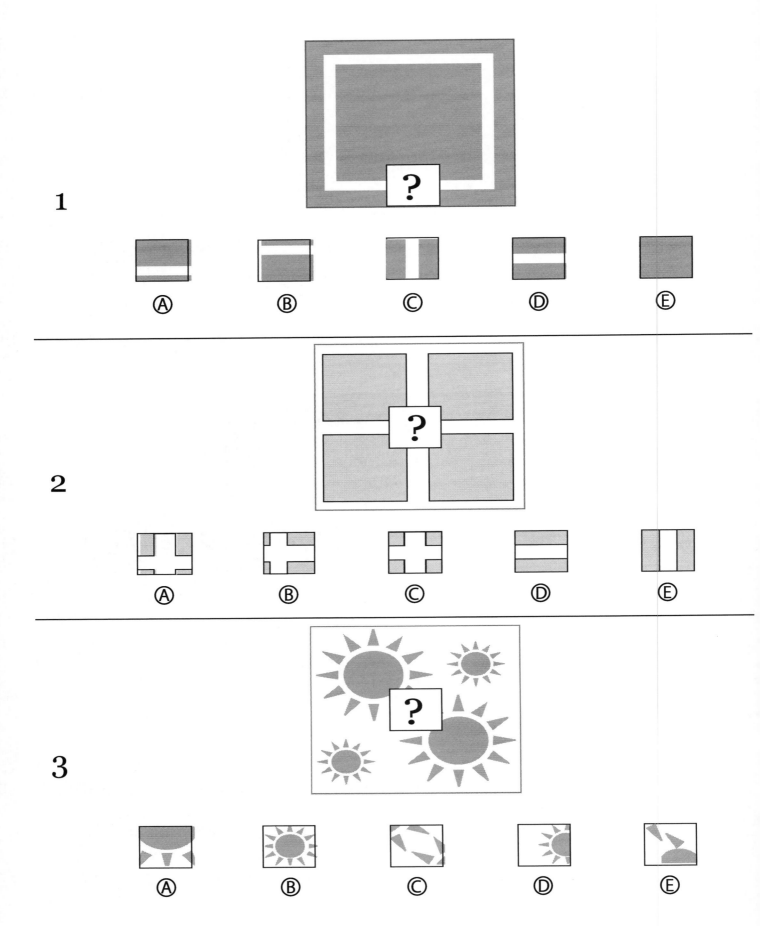

1

2

3

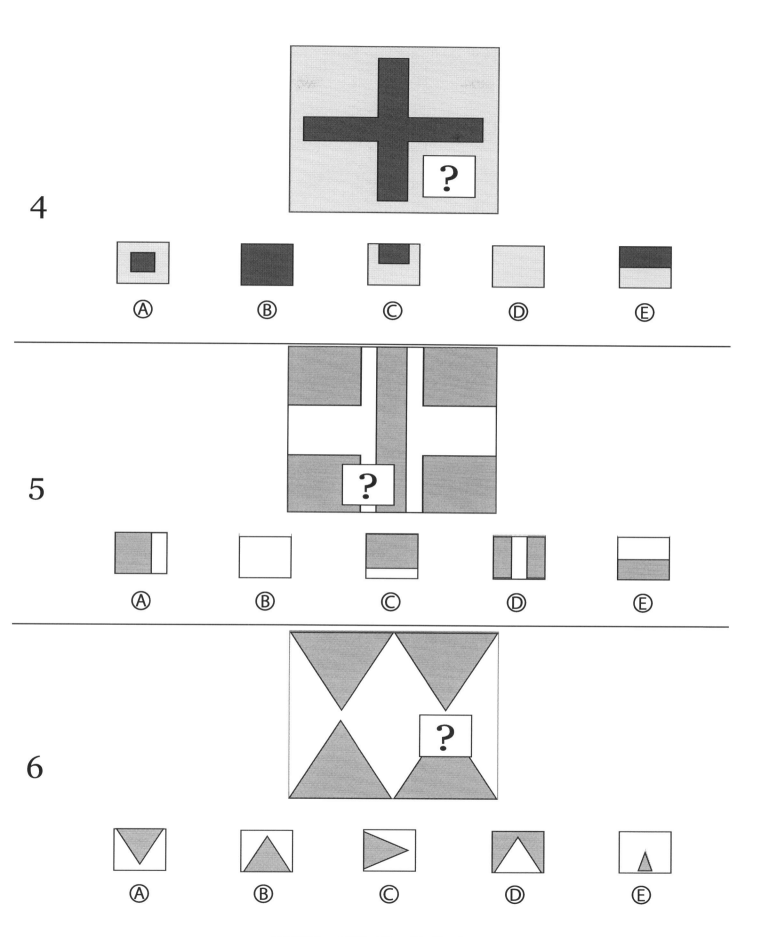

4

5

6

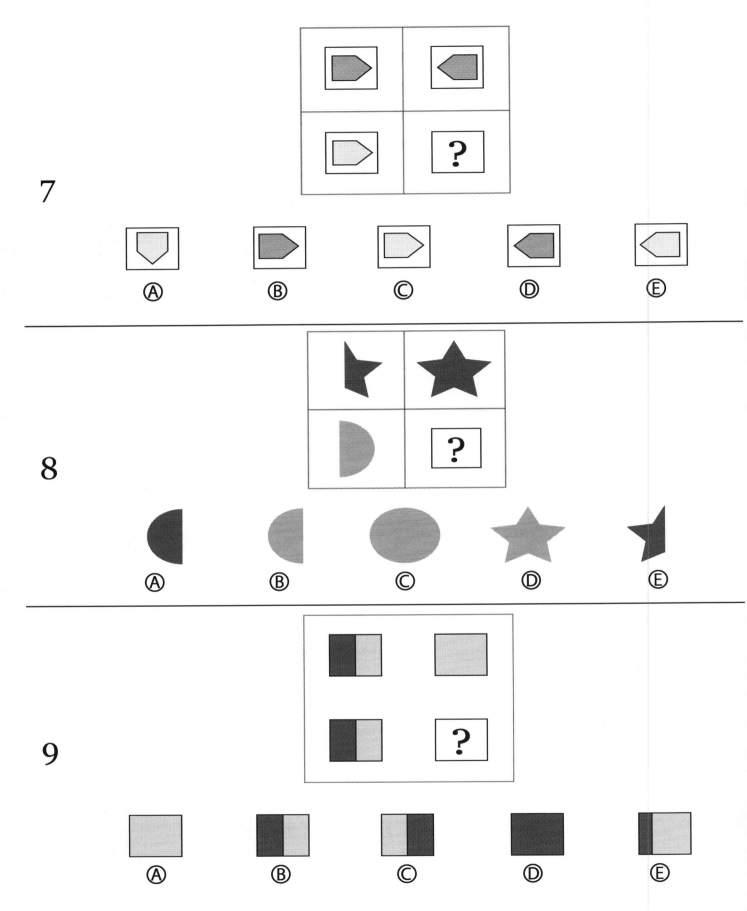

7

8

9

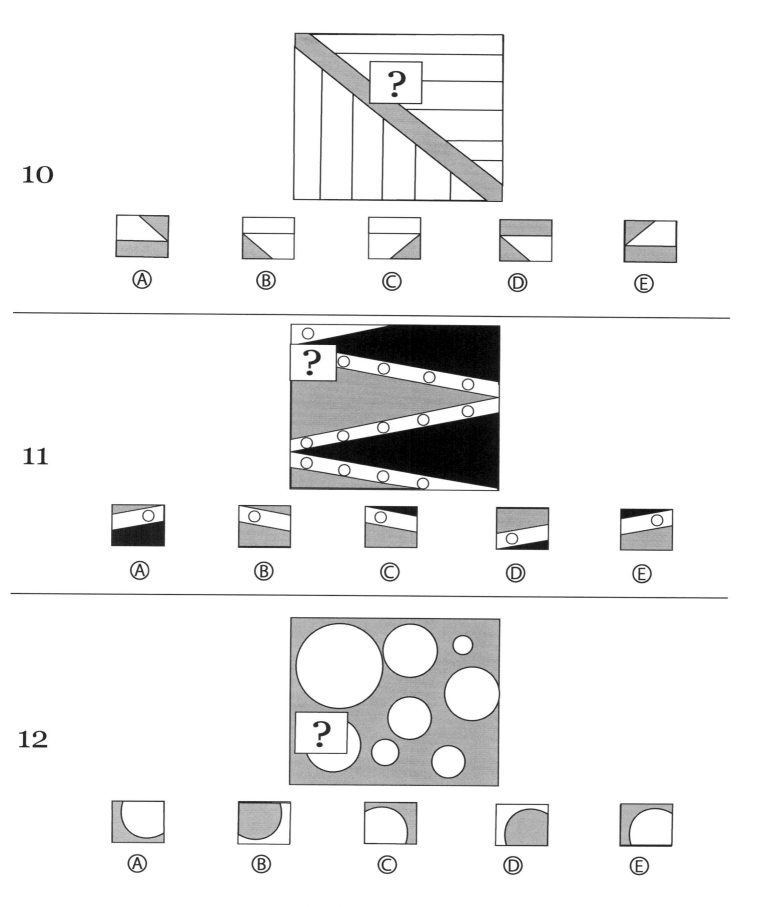

10

11

12

13

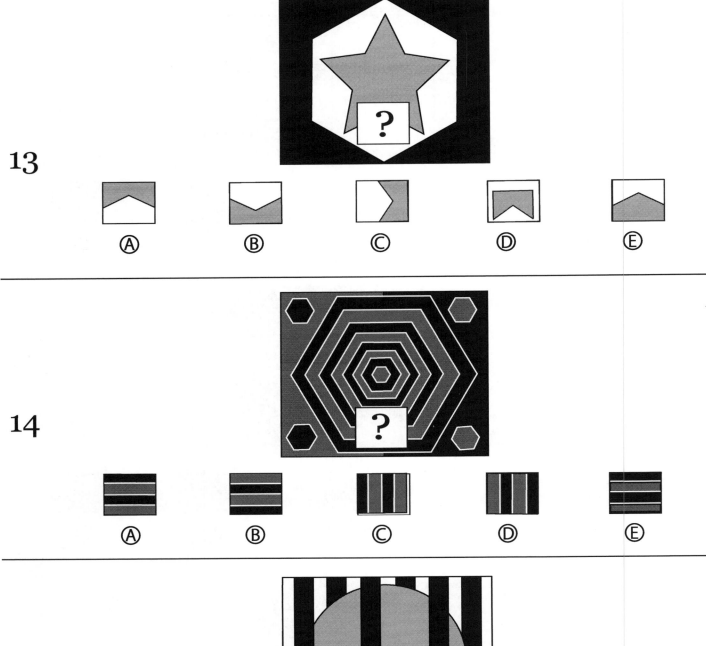

14

15

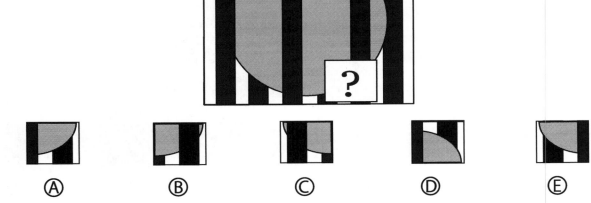

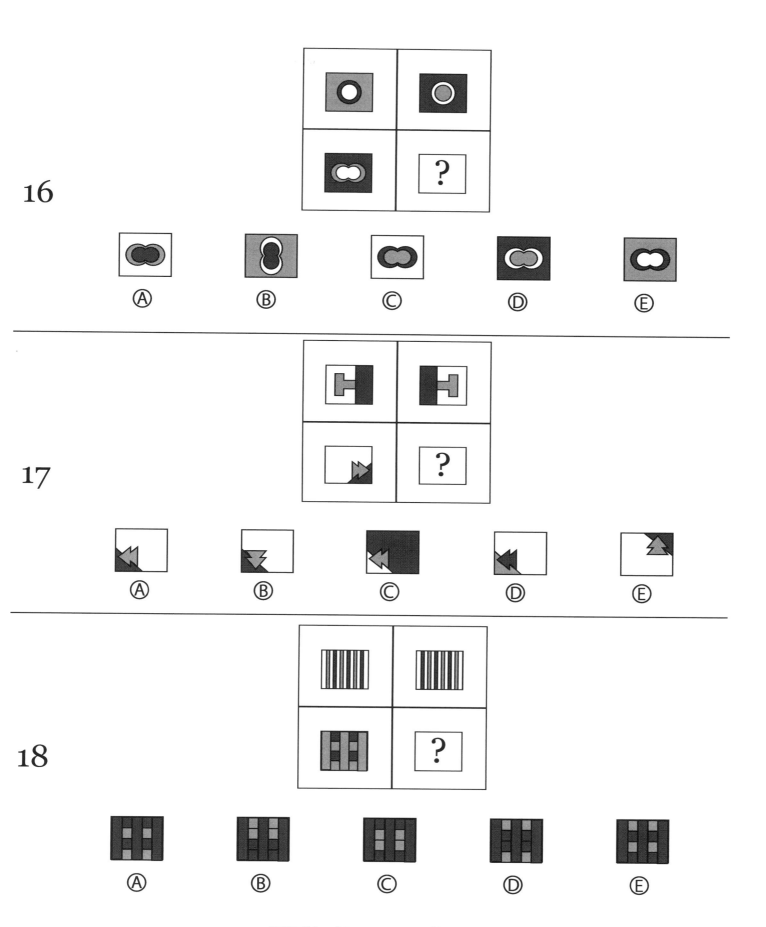

16

17

18

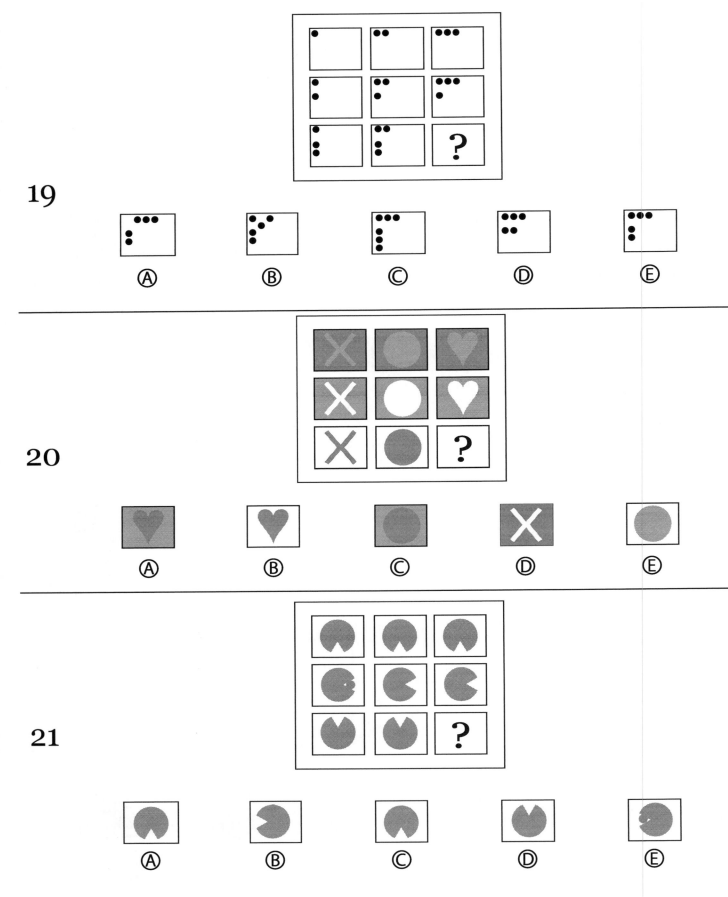

19

20

21

NNAT® Level B Test Prep Workbook

22

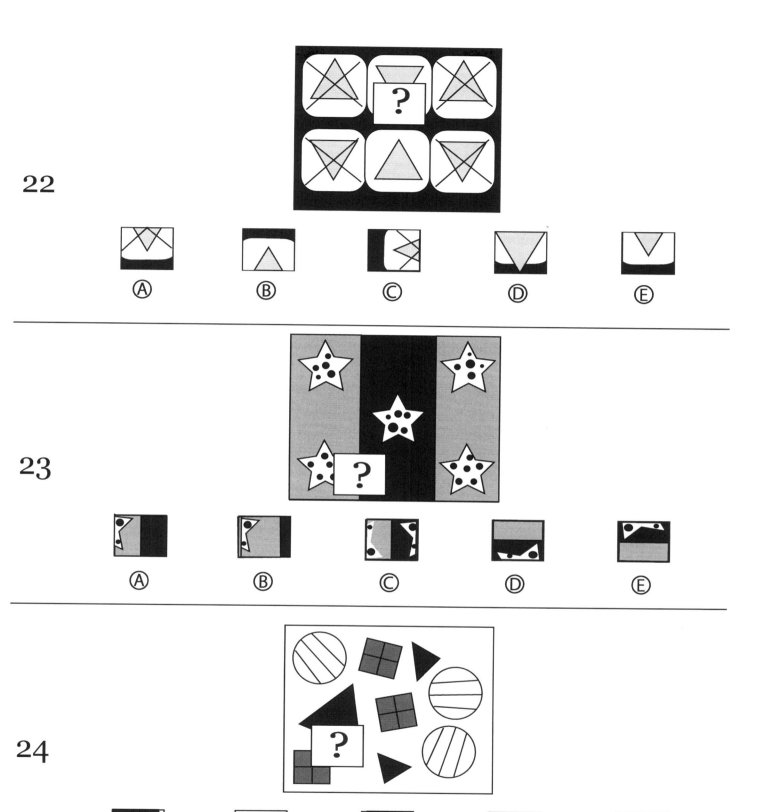

Ⓐ Ⓑ Ⓒ Ⓓ Ⓔ

23

Ⓐ Ⓑ Ⓒ Ⓓ Ⓔ

24

Ⓐ Ⓑ Ⓒ Ⓓ Ⓔ

25

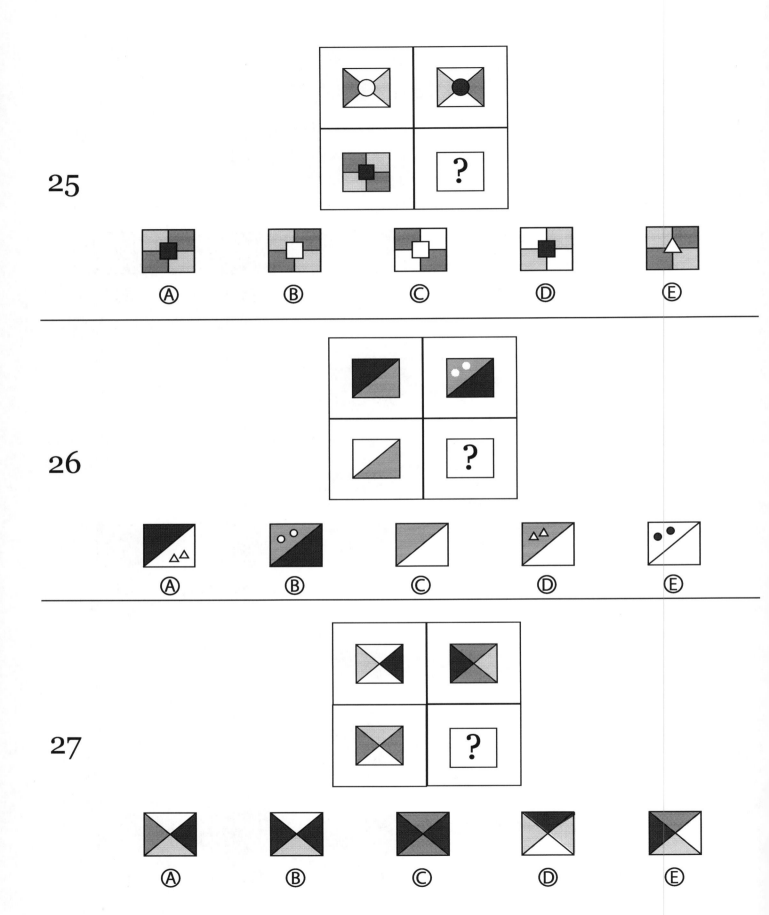

Ⓐ   Ⓑ   Ⓒ   Ⓓ   Ⓔ

26

Ⓐ   Ⓑ   Ⓒ   Ⓓ   Ⓔ

27

Ⓐ   Ⓑ   Ⓒ   Ⓓ   Ⓔ

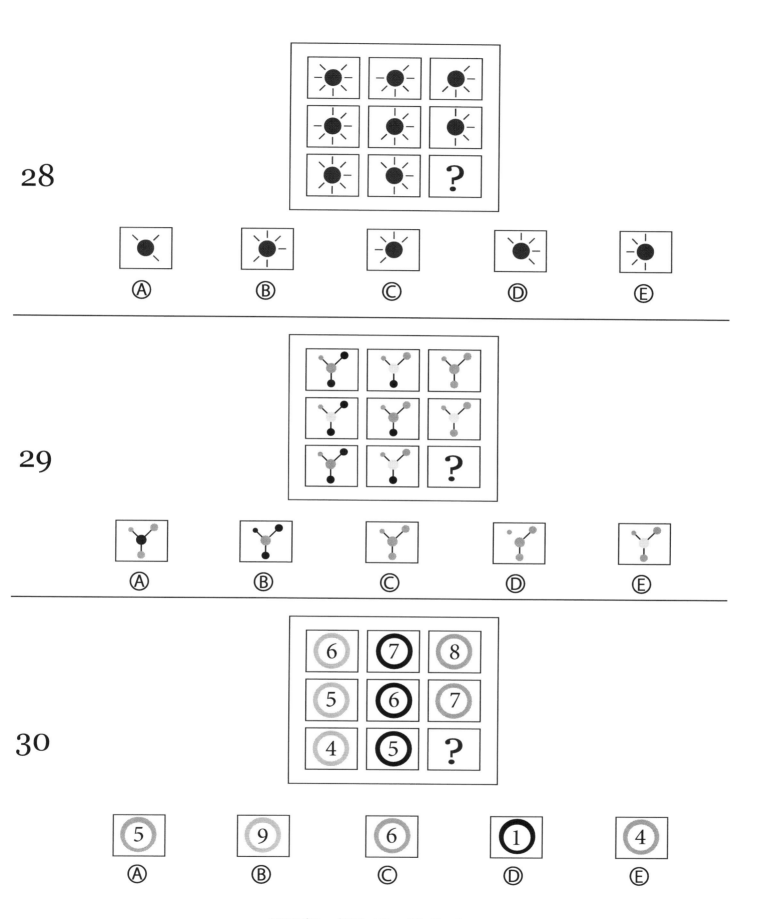

28

29

30

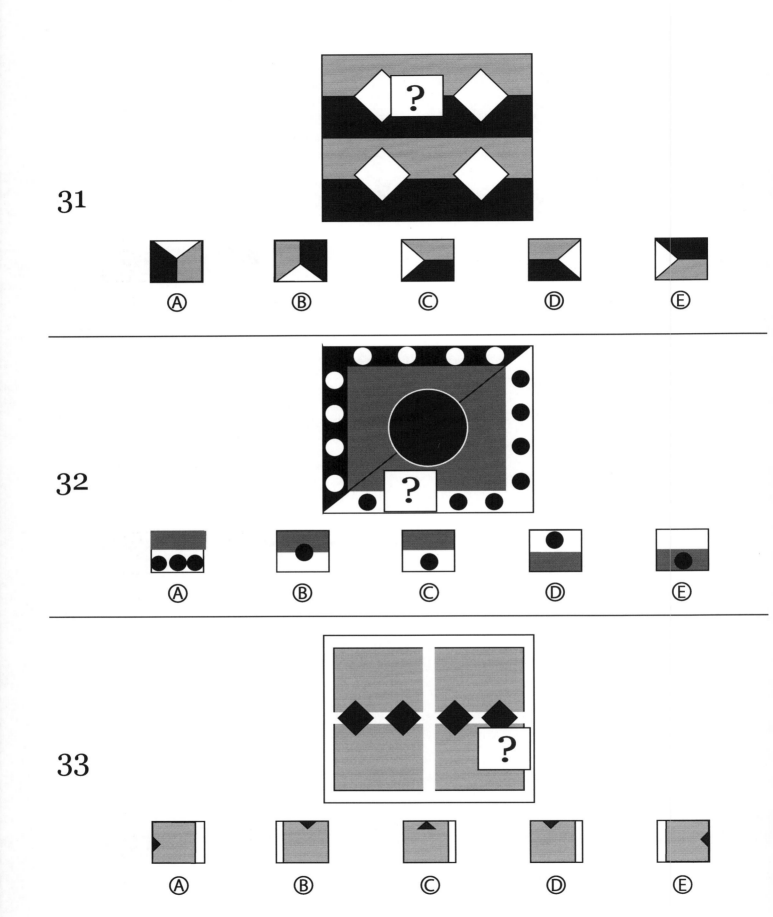

31

32

33

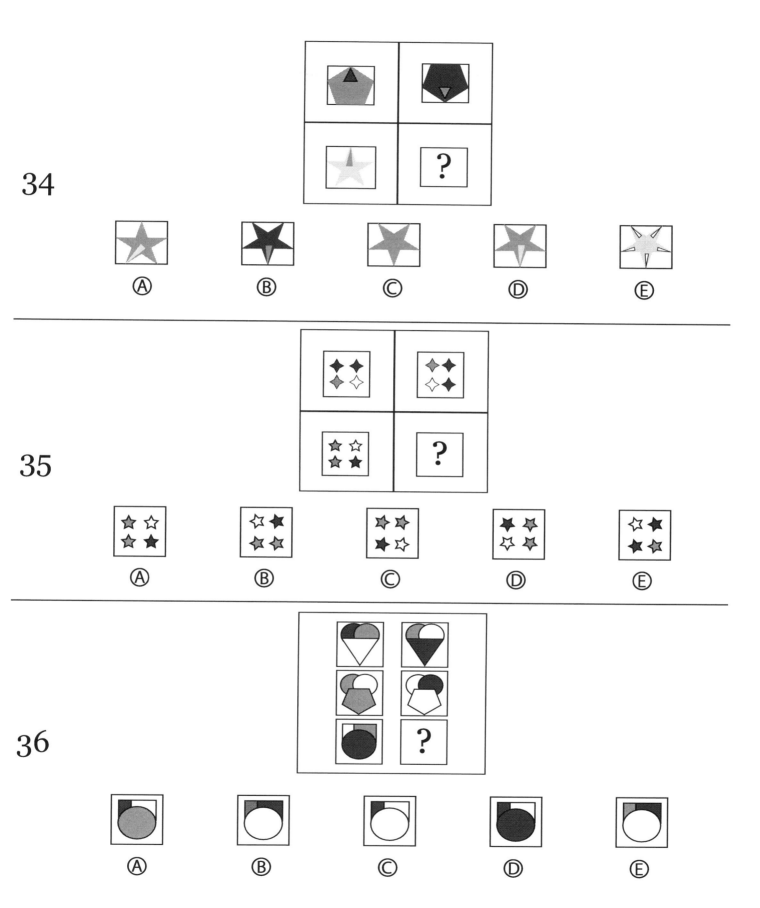

34

35

36

37

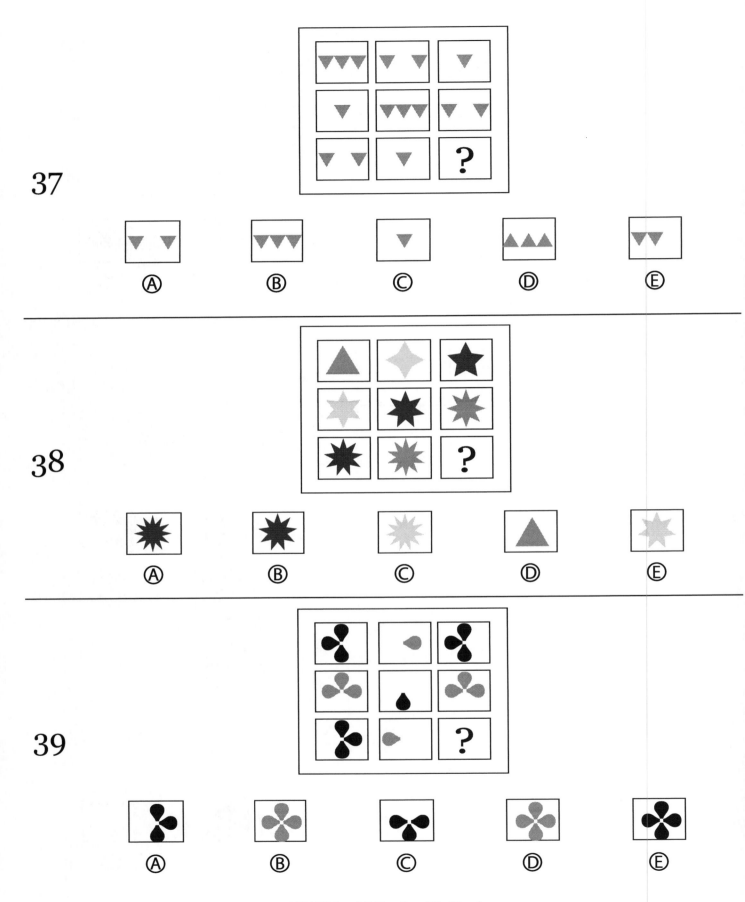

Ⓐ   Ⓑ   Ⓒ   Ⓓ   Ⓔ

38

Ⓐ   Ⓑ   Ⓒ   Ⓓ   Ⓔ

39

Ⓐ   Ⓑ   Ⓒ   Ⓓ   Ⓔ

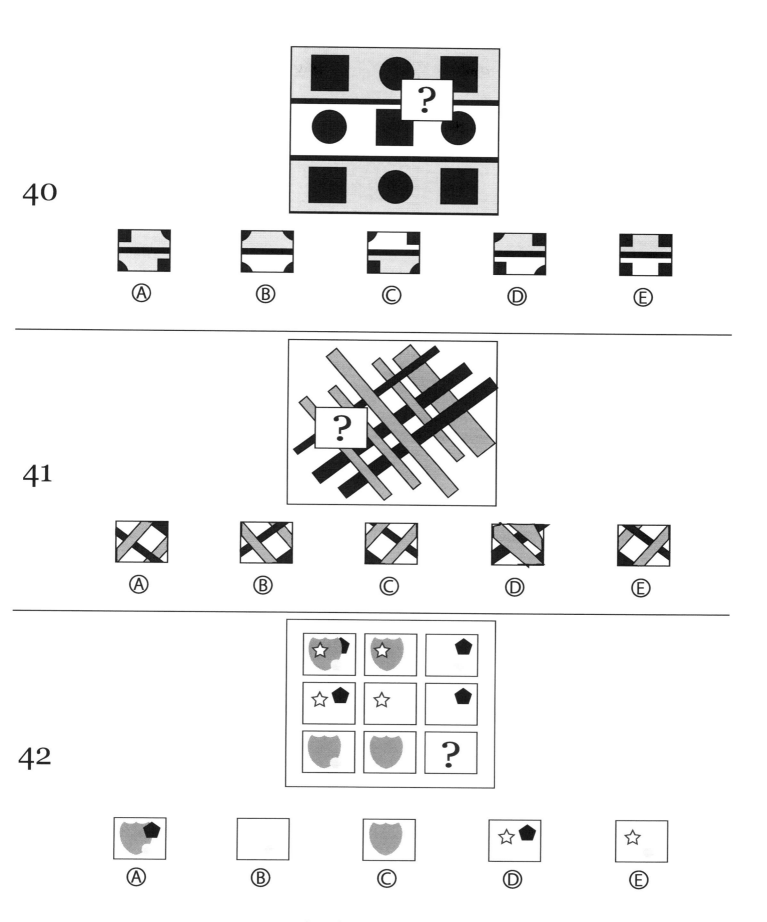

40

41

42

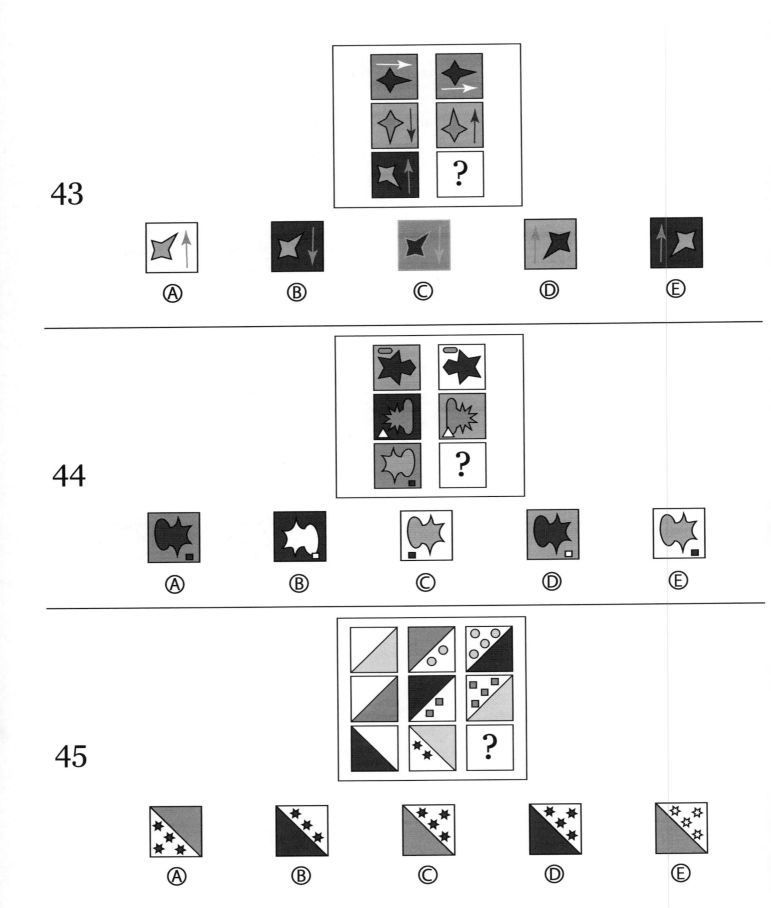

43

44

45

NNAT® Level B Test Prep Workbook

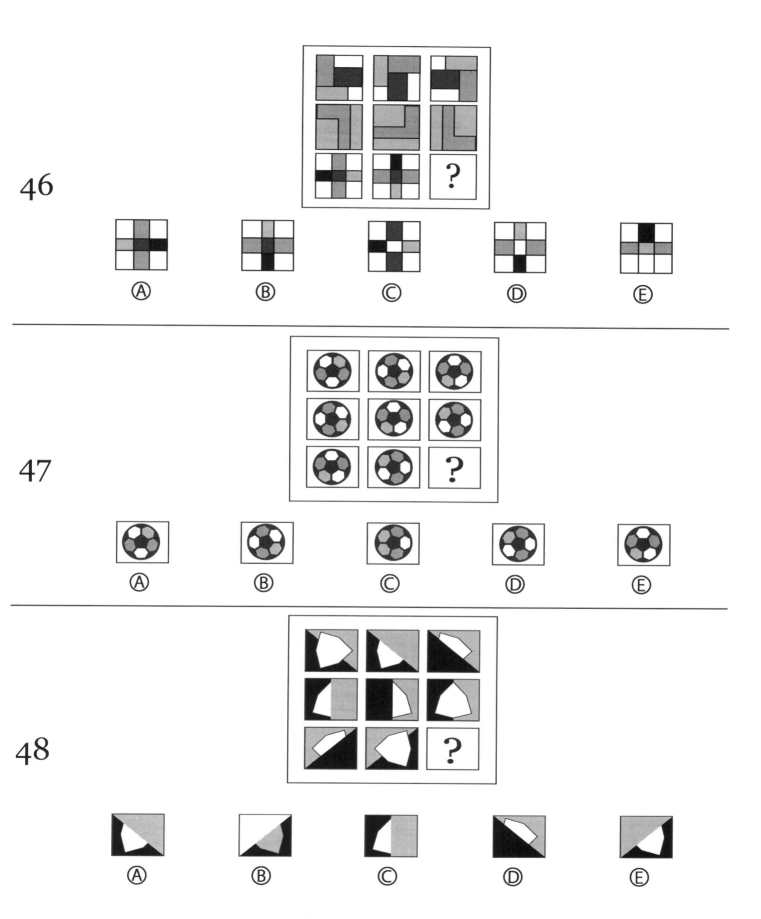

46

47

48

NNAT® Level B Bubble Sheets & Answers

Name:_____ Date:_____

1. Ⓐ Ⓑ Ⓒ Ⓓ Ⓔ   26. Ⓐ Ⓑ Ⓒ Ⓓ Ⓔ
2. Ⓐ Ⓑ Ⓒ Ⓓ Ⓔ   27. Ⓐ Ⓑ Ⓒ Ⓓ Ⓔ
3. Ⓐ Ⓑ Ⓒ Ⓓ Ⓔ   28. Ⓐ Ⓑ Ⓒ Ⓓ Ⓔ
4. Ⓐ Ⓑ Ⓒ Ⓓ Ⓔ   29. Ⓐ Ⓑ Ⓒ Ⓓ Ⓔ
5. Ⓐ Ⓑ Ⓒ Ⓓ Ⓔ   30. Ⓐ Ⓑ Ⓒ Ⓓ Ⓔ
6. Ⓐ Ⓑ Ⓒ Ⓓ Ⓔ   31. Ⓐ Ⓑ Ⓒ Ⓓ Ⓔ
7. Ⓐ Ⓑ Ⓒ Ⓓ Ⓔ   32. Ⓐ Ⓑ Ⓒ Ⓓ Ⓔ
8. Ⓐ Ⓑ Ⓒ Ⓓ Ⓔ   33. Ⓐ Ⓑ Ⓒ Ⓓ Ⓔ
9. Ⓐ Ⓑ Ⓒ Ⓓ Ⓔ   34. Ⓐ Ⓑ Ⓒ Ⓓ Ⓔ
10. Ⓐ Ⓑ Ⓒ Ⓓ Ⓔ   35. Ⓐ Ⓑ Ⓒ Ⓓ Ⓔ
11. Ⓐ Ⓑ Ⓒ Ⓓ Ⓔ   36. Ⓐ Ⓑ Ⓒ Ⓓ Ⓔ
12. Ⓐ Ⓑ Ⓒ Ⓓ Ⓔ   37. Ⓐ Ⓑ Ⓒ Ⓓ Ⓔ
13. Ⓐ Ⓑ Ⓒ Ⓓ Ⓔ   38. Ⓐ Ⓑ Ⓒ Ⓓ Ⓔ
14. Ⓐ Ⓑ Ⓒ Ⓓ Ⓔ   39. Ⓐ Ⓑ Ⓒ Ⓓ Ⓔ
15. Ⓐ Ⓑ Ⓒ Ⓓ Ⓔ   40. Ⓐ Ⓑ Ⓒ Ⓓ Ⓔ
16. Ⓐ Ⓑ Ⓒ Ⓓ Ⓔ   41. Ⓐ Ⓑ Ⓒ Ⓓ Ⓔ
17. Ⓐ Ⓑ Ⓒ Ⓓ Ⓔ   42. Ⓐ Ⓑ Ⓒ Ⓓ Ⓔ
18. Ⓐ Ⓑ Ⓒ Ⓓ Ⓔ   43. Ⓐ Ⓑ Ⓒ Ⓓ Ⓔ
19. Ⓐ Ⓑ Ⓒ Ⓓ Ⓔ   44. Ⓐ Ⓑ Ⓒ Ⓓ Ⓔ
20. Ⓐ Ⓑ Ⓒ Ⓓ Ⓔ   45. Ⓐ Ⓑ Ⓒ Ⓓ Ⓔ
21. Ⓐ Ⓑ Ⓒ Ⓓ Ⓔ   46. Ⓐ Ⓑ Ⓒ Ⓓ Ⓔ
22. Ⓐ Ⓑ Ⓒ Ⓓ Ⓔ   47. Ⓐ Ⓑ Ⓒ Ⓓ Ⓔ
23. Ⓐ Ⓑ Ⓒ Ⓓ Ⓔ   48. Ⓐ Ⓑ Ⓒ Ⓓ Ⓔ
24. Ⓐ Ⓑ Ⓒ Ⓓ Ⓔ
25. Ⓐ Ⓑ Ⓒ Ⓓ Ⓔ

Name:_____   Date:_____

1. (A) (B) (C) (D) (E)   26. (A) (B) (C) (D) (E)
2. (A) (B) (C) (D) (E)   27. (A) (B) (C) (D) (E)
3. (A) (B) (C) (D) (E)   28. (A) (B) (C) (D) (E)
4. (A) (B) (C) (D) (E)   29. (A) (B) (C) (D) (E)
5. (A) (B) (C) (D) (E)   30. (A) (B) (C) (D) (E)
6. (A) (B) (C) (D) (E)   31. (A) (B) (C) (D) (E)
7. (A) (B) (C) (D) (E)   32. (A) (B) (C) (D) (E)
8. (A) (B) (C) (D) (E)   33. (A) (B) (C) (D) (E)
9. (A) (B) (C) (D) (E)   34. (A) (B) (C) (D) (E)
10. (A) (B) (C) (D) (E)   35. (A) (B) (C) (D) (E)
11. (A) (B) (C) (D) (E)   36. (A) (B) (C) (D) (E)
12. (A) (B) (C) (D) (E)   37. (A) (B) (C) (D) (E)
13. (A) (B) (C) (D) (E)   38. (A) (B) (C) (D) (E)
14. (A) (B) (C) (D) (E)   39. (A) (B) (C) (D) (E)
15. (A) (B) (C) (D) (E)   40. (A) (B) (C) (D) (E)
16. (A) (B) (C) (D) (E)   41. (A) (B) (C) (D) (E)
17. (A) (B) (C) (D) (E)   42. (A) (B) (C) (D) (E)
18. (A) (B) (C) (D) (E)   43. (A) (B) (C) (D) (E)
19. (A) (B) (C) (D) (E)   44. (A) (B) (C) (D) (E)
20. (A) (B) (C) (D) (E)   45. (A) (B) (C) (D) (E)
21. (A) (B) (C) (D) (E)   46. (A) (B) (C) (D) (E)
22. (A) (B) (C) (D) (E)   47. (A) (B) (C) (D) (E)
23. (A) (B) (C) (D) (E)   48. (A) (B) (C) (D) (E)
24. (A) (B) (C) (D) (E)
25. (A) (B) (C) (D) (E)

Answer Explanations. Test One.

Please note that there are often various ways to solve the puzzles. These answer explantions provide one option for solving each puzzle.

The answer explanations provide the correct answer for both the 'color' and 'black and white' versions of the book (the black/white/ gray shade are referenced, when relevant, in brackets).

Download a color version of this book at:
https://originstutoring.lpages.co/nnat110

1. **E.** The puzzle piece completes the pattern.

2. **C.** The puzzle piece completes the pattern.

3. **D.** The puzzle piece completes the pattern.

4. **B.** The puzzle piece completes the pattern.

5. **D.** The puzzle piece completes the pattern.

6. **A.** The puzzle piece completes the pattern.

7. **A.** Moving across the rows, the blue (gray) pentagon becomes a blue (gray) star.

8. **A.** Across the rows, the light blue (light gray) shape become dark blue (dark gray), and dark blue(dark gray) shapes become light blue (light gray).

9. **E.** The arrows are mirrored.

10. **C.** Moving across the row, the shape turns 90 degrees clockwise, and the background and foreground shape swap colors.

11. **A.** In the left box, the figure has one color/ shade. Moving to the middle row, the figure incorporates a smaller white inner figure of the same shape. The right box incorporates a third even smaller figure of the same shape with the original color/shade.

12. **B.** In the matrix, the figures (background square with interlocking figures of same shape and size) change across the row and down the columns. The background color/shade of the square behind the interlocking shapes also alternate color/shade across the rows and down the columns.

13. **D.** The puzzle piece completes the pattern.

14. **B.** The puzzle piece completes the pattern.

15. **E.** The puzzle piece completes the pattern.

16. **E.** The puzzle piece completes the pattern.

17. **D.** The puzzle piece completes the pattern.

18. **A.** The puzzle piece completes the pattern.

19. **C.** The number of sides of the shapes on the left corresponds to the number of points of the figures on the right. Moving across the rows, the color of the shape changes from dark blue (dark gray) to light blue (light gray).

20. **B.** The number of points of the figure on the left corresponds with the number of shapes on the right. Moving across the rows, the colors change from orange (medium gray) to white.

21. **A.** The shapes are mirrored from left to right.

22. **B.** In the matrix, from left to right, you see that the figures change across the row. The shade of each figure is different across the rows, and down the columns.

23. **C.** Moving from the left row to the middle row, the smaller circle stays in the same place in relationship to the larger circle. From the middle row to the right row, the small circle rotates clockwise around the edge of the larger circle. Down the columns, the smaller circle rotates clockwise around the edge of the larger circle.

24. **D.** Across the rows, the middle and bottom shapes move toward the opposite edge. Down the columns, the shape/line becomes distorted.

25. **E.** The puzzle piece completes the pattern.

26. **B.** The puzzle piece completes the pattern.

27. **E.** The puzzle piece completes the pattern.

28. **B.** The puzzle piece completes the pattern.

29. **B.** The puzzle piece completes the pattern.

30. **C.** The puzzle piece completes the pattern.

31. **E.** Moving from left to right box, the colors of the shapes are inverted.

32. **E.** The colors/shades of the two figures are inverted in the identical figures on the right.

33. **E.** The colors/shades are inverted from left to right.

34. **E.** Across the rows, the number of points on the outer star decrease by one. Down the columns, the points on the inner star increase by one.

35. **B.** Across the rows, the group of shapes rotate counterclockwise. Down the columns, the group of shapes rotate counterclockwise while the shapes within the group become more round.

36. **A.** Both across and down, the triangles alternate between groups of 1, 2 and 3 triangles and between 3 patterns.

37. **E.** The puzzle piece completes the pattern.

38. **B.** The puzzle piece completes the pattern.

39. **C.** The puzzle piece completes the pattern.

40. **A.** The puzzle piece completes the pattern.

41. **E.** The puzzle piece completes the pattern.

42. **D.** The puzzle piece completes the pattern.

43. **C.** There are no changes in the larger figures from left to right. There is a change of shade/color in the smaller figure (it gets lighter).

44. **D.** The number of squares on the left correlate with the points of the star on the right.

45. **B.** The figures are reflected along the vertical axis and the colors/shades inverted.

46. **C.** The number of shapes increases by two from left to right.

47. **C.** Across, the outermost circle alternates between black, medium gray and light gray while the innermost circle alternates between black and medium gray. Down, the center circle (white) expands while the innermost circle alternates between black and medium gray.

48. **A.** Across, the small circle moves past the larger circle. Down, the smaller circle increases in size.

Answer Explanations. Test Two.

1. **D.** The puzzle piece completes the pattern.

2. **C.** The puzzle piece completes the pattern.

3. **C.** The puzzle piece completes the pattern.

4. **D.** The puzzle piece completes the pattern.

5. **D.** The puzzle piece completes the pattern.

6. **B.** The puzzle piece completes the pattern.

7. **E.** The figure is reflected or flips 180 degrees.

8. **C.** The half figure becomes a full figure.

9. **A.** In the left box, the figure has two equal halves each with a different shade/color. The right box contains the same figure with one shade/color (from the right half of the original figure).

10. **B.** The puzzle piece completes the pattern.

11. **C.** The puzzle piece completes the pattern.

12. **E.** The puzzle piece completes the pattern.

13. **A.** The puzzle piece completes the pattern.

14. **B.** The puzzle piece completes the pattern.

15. **B.** The puzzle piece completes the pattern.

16. **C.** In the top left hand box is a square with two circles inside. Moving from the left to right box, the shapes swap colors. Orange (medium gray) becomes blue (dark gray), blue (dark gray) becomes white and white becomes orange (medium gray).

17. **A.** In the top left hand box there are two shapes with different colors/shades. Moving from the left to right box, the shapes are flipped horizontally, retaining the color of the shapes.

18. **E.** Moving from left to right box, the colors of the shapes are inverted. The other answer options are incorrect becuase the orange (medium gray) parts of the shape are incorrectly located vis a vis the inital shape in bottom left box.

19. **E.** One circle is added from left to right and one circle is added from top to bottom.

20. **B.** The shape changes across the rows while the shape and background colors/shades change down the columns.

21. **D.** Across the rows, the smaller circle moves from right to left while down the columns the larger shape rotates counterclockwise 90 degrees.

22. **E.** The puzzle piece completes the pattern.

23. **A.** The puzzle piece completes the pattern.

24. **A.** The puzzle piece completes the pattern.

25. **B.** Moving from the left to right box, the shape is flipped horizontally. A shape in the middle of the figure changes its color.

26. **D.** In the top left hand box is a square divided into halves, each with a different color. Moving from the left to right box, the colors of the halves are inverted and two small shapes (of the same shape) are added.

27. **B.** Moving from the left to right box, the same colored triangles change to a new color/ shade and the colors of the other two triangles are inverted.

28. **D.** Across the rows, the lines around the circle disappear in a counter clockwise direction.

29. **C.** The outer circles become green (medium gray) in a clockwise direction across the rows while the inner circle alternates between green (medium gray) and light blue (light gray)

30. **C.** Across each row, the outer circles change colors/shades as the numbers increase by 1 while the numbers in the columns decrease by 1 from top to bottom.

31. **C.** The puzzle piece completes the pattern.

32. **C.** The puzzle piece completes the pattern.

33. **D.** The puzzle piece completes the pattern.

34. **D.** In the top left hand box is a pentagon with a triangle at one of its corners. Moving from the left to right box, the pentagon is turned upside down and the pentagon and the triangles swap their colors.

35. **C.** Moving from the left to right box, the 4 stars are rotated 90 degree clockwise.

36. **A.** Moving from the left to right box, the color pattern changes. Dark blue (dark gray) becomes orange (medium gray) , orange (medium gray) becomes white, and white becomes dark blue (dark gray) .

37. **B.** The triangles alternate in number across each row and down each column.

38. **C.** The shape increases by one point across each row while the colors/shades of the shapes alternate between shades/colors both across and down.

39. **A.** Across the rows the shapes alternate between colors/shades and 1 and 3 "petals",

while down the columns the shapes alternate between colors/shades and rotate clockwise.

40. **D.** The puzzle piece completes the pattern.

41. **B.** The puzzle piece completes the pattern.

42. **B.** The third and second columns across the rows combine to make the groups of shapes in the first column, while the bottom and middle rows in each column combine to make the groups of shapes at the top of the columns.

43. **B.** Moving from the left to right box, the color pattern is retained, but the shapes are flipped vertically.

44. **E.** Moving from the left to right box, the color of the background changes, however the color of the two shapes is retained. The complex shape is flipped horizontally while the smaller shape is left undisturbed at the same position.

45. **C.** Across the rows, the triangles alternate between 3 shades/colors. The position of the triangles alternate between two positions. Two smaller shapes are added in the middle box, and two more smaller shapes (of the same color) are added in the far right box (to add up to four small shapes in the far right box).

46. **A.** Across the rows, the shape is rotated 90 clockwise.

47. **A.** The soccer ball rotates clockwise across each row and down each column.

48. **E.** The triangles of the background hide part of the geometric shape. Across the row, the geometric white shape is either shown fully or is partially hidden.

DOWNLOAD THE PRACTICE TEST/S
IN COLOR

If you also want the COLOR version of this book, please go to the following link to download it!

Please visit
https://originstutoring.lpages.co/nnat110
to access a color version of your practice test/s.

**Thank you for selecting this book.
We would be thrilled if you left us a review on the website where you bought this book!**

Made in the
USA
Middletown, DE